Contents

Printed in China

ISBN: 978-1-897164-78-5

Test-taking TIPS

General

- Count the number of pages to make sure that there are no missing pages.

- Read the instructions carefully so that you know what to do and how to do it.

- Write neatly.

- Always check your answers and writing after you have completed the test.

- Skip the questions that you are stuck on and come back to them after completing the rest of the test.

MULTIPLE CHOICE

- Read through the test quickly. Skip the difficult questions and do the easy ones first.

- Read the question twice before finding the answer.

- Look for keywords in the question. (e.g. "fewer" suggests a subtraction problem; "share...equally" suggests a division problem)

- Come up with the answer in your head before looking at the possible answers.

- Read all the four options before deciding which is the correct answer.

- Eliminate the options that you know are incorrect.

ISBN: 978-1-897164-78-5

PROBLEM SOLVING

- Read the whole question carefully and never make any assumptions about what the question might be.

- Highlight (i.e. underline / circle) the important information in the question.

- Translate the words into mathematical terms.

- Use drawings to help you better understand the question.

- Break down the problem into several parts and solve them one by one.

- Know exactly what needs to be included in your solution.

- Estimate the answer.

- Before writing out the solution, organize your thoughts.

- For a question that involves measurements,

  – make sure the measurements are uniform when solving the problem.
  – the measurement in the answer is converted to the unit that is asked.

- Use words to describe what you are calculating.

- Always write a concluding sentence for your solution.

- Check if your answer is reasonable (i.e. Is the answer close to your estimate?).

- Never leave a question blank. Show your work or write down your thoughts. Even if you do not get the correct answer, you might get some marks for your work.

ISBN: 978-1-897164-78-5

1 Look at the money that Sue has.

How many quarters can Sue trade at the most?

- o 14
- o 10
- o 15
- o 12

2 Which point shows 615 on the number line?

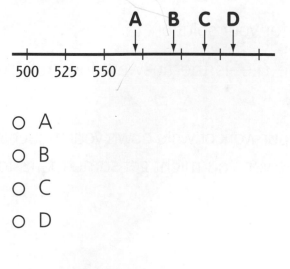

- o A
- o B
- o C
- o D

3 Look at the ribbon below.

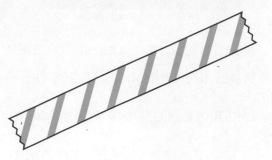

Measure to find the length of the ribbon.

- o a bit longer than 6 cm
- o a bit shorter than 7 cm
- o exactly 7 cm
- o a bit longer than 7 cm

4 Which figure can be formed using the net below?

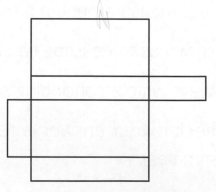

- o triangular pyramid
- o rectangular prism
- o square-based prism
- o cube

ISBN: 978-1-897164-78-5

5 The clock below shows the the time when Michael finished his breakfast.

What time did Michael start his breakfast?

○ 8:00

○ 7:15

○ 6:20

○ 7:45

6 Kevin uses estimation to solve the following problem.

$$341 - 289$$

Which is closest to the difference?

○ 340 – 280

○ 350 – 290

○ 350 – 280

○ 340 – 290

7 Look at the pattern.

Figure 1   Figure 2   Figure 3

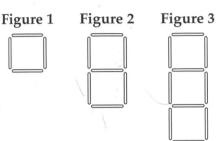

Follow the pattern to find the number of sticks in Figure 5.

○ 16

○ 13

○ 15

○ 14

8 Leo has a bag of 15 marbles. The marbles are either red or yellow. The number of red marbles doubles the number of yellow marbles. Leo draws a marble from the bag without looking. Which best describes the chance that Leo gets a yellow marble?

○ certain

○ likely

○ unlikely

○ impossible

ISBN: 978-1-897164-78-5

1

9 Linda and Andy use pictographs to record their stickers. Look at their pictographs.

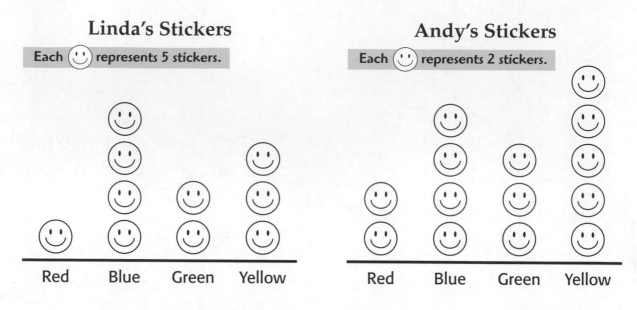

Andy thinks that he has more stickers than Linda. Is he right?

Explain Your Thinking

ISBN: 978-1-897164-78-5

10 This list shows the number of apples that each customer buys.

8	16	5	3	7	10	21	17
3	15	18	18	2	24	15	13
14	11	7	19	2	14	13	12

Organize the data in the tally chart. What is the range of the number of apples that most customers buy?

Show Your Work

Number of Apples	Number of Customers
1 – 5	
6 – 10	
11 – 15	
16 – 20	
21 – 25	

ISBN: 978-1-897164-78-5

1 Mr. Smith always takes a walk of 20 minutes after dinner. If Mr. Smith finished his walk at 7:10 p.m. tonight, what time did he start his walk?

- ○ 6:30 p.m.
- ○ 6:50 p.m.
- ○ 7:30 p.m.
- ○ 6:50 a.m.

2 Jason is finding the answer to this subtraction sentence.

$$58 - 27 = \boxed{}$$

Which number sentence should he use to check the answer?

- ○ 58 + 27 = 85
- ○ 31 + 27 = 58
- ○ 58 − 25 = 33
- ○ 31 + 27 + 27 = 58 + 27

3 There are 463 red balls and 209 blue balls in a box. If Judy takes out 243 balls from the box, how many balls will be left?

- ○ 11
- ○ 429
- ○ 497
- ○ 915

4 Erin wants to build a pyramid using all of the following sticks and modelling clay.

Which pyramid can she build?

- ○ triangular pyramid
- ○ rectangular pyramid
- ○ pentagonal pyramid
- ○ hexagonal pyramid

ISBN: 978-1-897164-78-5

5 The graph shows the results of a survey of the children's favourite food for lunch.

Our Favourite Food for Lunch

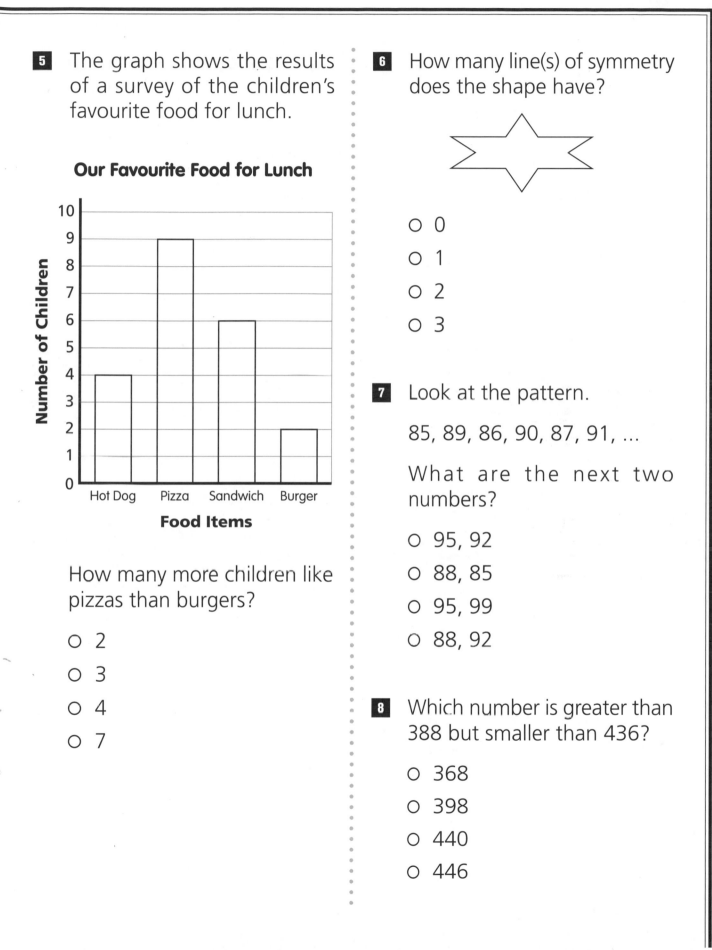

How many more children like pizzas than burgers?

○ 2

○ 3

○ 4

○ 7

6 How many line(s) of symmetry does the shape have?

○ 0

○ 1

○ 2

○ 3

7 Look at the pattern.

85, 89, 86, 90, 87, 91, ...

What are the next two numbers?

○ 95, 92

○ 88, 85

○ 95, 99

○ 88, 92

8 Which number is greater than 388 but smaller than 436?

○ 368

○ 398

○ 440

○ 446

ISBN: 978-1-897164-78-5

2

9 There are 17 children in Mrs. Smith's senior kindergarten class. Mrs. Smith needs helpers for a class outing. Each helper takes care of 5 children.

How many helpers does Mrs. Smith need?

Use a diagram to illustrate your answer.

Explain Your Thinking

ISBN: 978-1-897164-78-5

10 Andrew sorted the figures into two groups. His sorting rule is "rectangular faces" and "6 vertices".

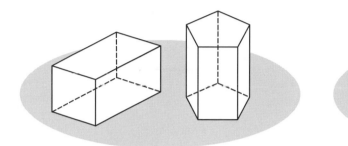
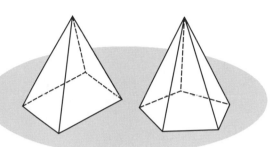

Rectangular Faces   **6 Vertices**

Andrew's friend, Kelly, found that he misplaced one figure. Name the misplaced figure and explain.

Explain Your Thinking

ISBN: 978-1-897164-78-5

1 Sarah filled 4 glasses with 1 litre of juice. How many glasses does she need to hold 6 litres of juice?

○ 4
○ 5
○ 24
○ 30

2 These are Judy's stickers.

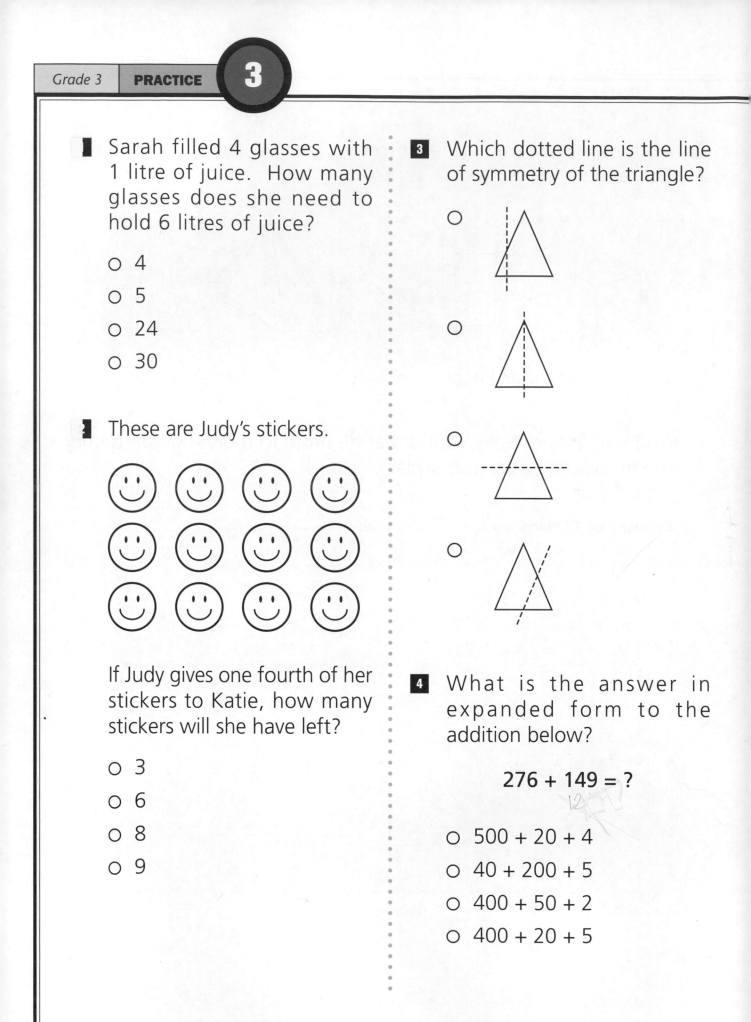

If Judy gives one fourth of her stickers to Katie, how many stickers will she have left?

○ 3
○ 6
○ 8
○ 9

3 Which dotted line is the line of symmetry of the triangle?

○

○

○

○

4 What is the answer in expanded form to the addition below?

276 + 149 = ?

○ 500 + 20 + 4
○ 40 + 200 + 5
○ 400 + 50 + 2
○ 400 + 20 + 5

ISBN: 978-1-897164-78-5

5 Look at the pattern.

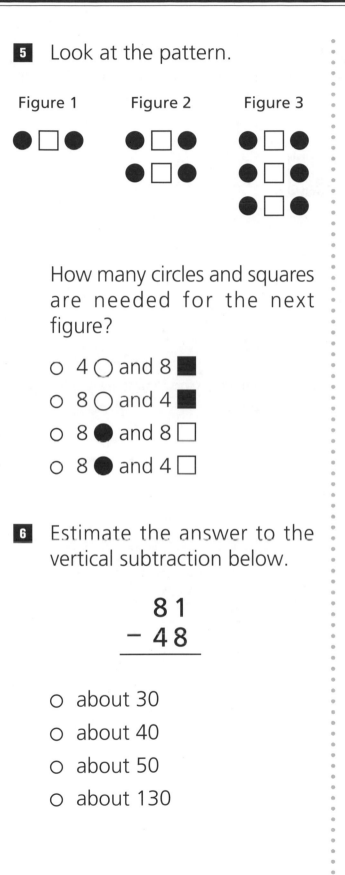

Figure 1   Figure 2   Figure 3

How many circles and squares are needed for the next figure?

- ○ 4 ◯ and 8 ■
- ○ 8 ◯ and 4 ■
- ○ 8 ● and 8 □
- ○ 8 ● and 4 □

6 Estimate the answer to the vertical subtraction below.

$$81$$
$$-48$$

- ○ about 30
- ○ about 40
- ○ about 50
- ○ about 130

7 Jane has 16 scarves. 4 of them are blue and 2 of them are red. She picks a scarf randomly without looking. What is the chance that the scarf she picks is not blue or red?

- ○ certain
- ○ likely
- ○ unlikely
- ○ impossible

8 Measure the sides of the shape below.

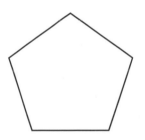

What is its perimeter in centimetres?

- ○ 5
- ○ 6
- ○ 10
- ○ 12

ISBN: 978-1-897164-78-5

9 ABC Department Store is going to hold a lucky draw. The saleswoman, Mrs. Dickson, has proposed two ways to put different balls in the box. The ways are as follows:

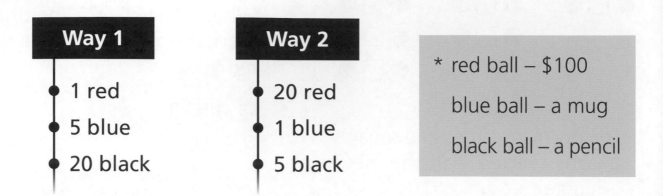

Way 1	Way 2	
• 1 red	• 20 red	* red ball – $100
• 5 blue	• 1 blue	blue ball – a mug
• 20 black	• 5 black	black ball – a pencil

If you were the manager of the store, which way would you use? Give reasons.

Explain Your Thinking

ISBN: 978-1-897164-78-5

14

10 Mr. White buys a newspaper on Saturday. Look at the coins that Mr. White has.

Sunny News	
Mon – Fri	$0.75 each
Sat	$1.25 each
Sun	$1.50 each

If Mr. White uses the fewest coins to pay for a newspaper, which coins will he have left? What is the total value?

Explain Your Thinking

ISBN: 978-1-897164-78-5

1 The dotted line is the line of symmetry of the L-shape.

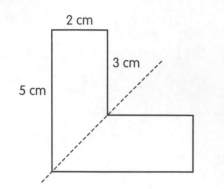

What is the perimeter of the L-shape?

○ 10 cm

○ 16 cm

○ 20 cm

○ 24 cm

2 Look at the pattern.

△ ⊙ ▯ △ ⊙ ▯ △ ⊙ ▯ △

Following the pattern, what are the next two shapes?

○ ⊙ ▯

○ ⊙ ▯

○ ⊙ ▯

○ ⊙ ▯

3 The clock shows the time that Judy starts practising the piano.

If Judy practises the piano for 35 minutes, at what time will she finish?

○ 4:10

○ 5:05

○ 5:20

○ 5:45

4 Jill pays a toonie for a hot dog which costs $1.75. What is her change?

○ a penny

○ a nickel

○ a dime

○ a quarter

ISBN: 978-1-897164-78-5

5 Which number is greater than 620 but smaller than 637?

- ○ 639
- ○ 617
- ○ 629
- ○ 699

6 Helen wants to make a pentagonal pyramid with straws and modelling clay.

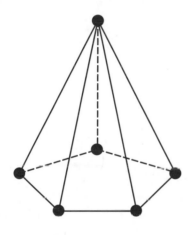

How many straws does she need?

- ○ 6
- ○ 10
- ○ 12
- ○ 15

7 The pictograph shows the number of stickers that the children have.

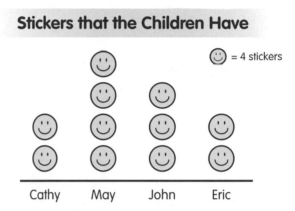

Stickers that the Children Have

☺ = 4 stickers

Cathy   May   John   Eric

How many stickers do the girls have in all?

- ○ 6
- ○ 20
- ○ 24
- ○ 44

8 Tim has 127 red paper clips and 52 green ones. If Eva has 34 more paper clips than Tim, how many paper clips does Eva have?

- ○ 145
- ○ 109
- ○ 41
- ○ 213

ISBN: 978-1-897164-78-5

4

9 Katie bought 16 lollipops on Wednesday. The number of lollipops that Katie bought on Thursday was 4 more than that on Wednesday.

Katie puts all the lollipops that she bought in these two days equally into 4 bags. How many lollipops are there in each bag?

Explain Your Thinking

ISBN: 978-1-897164-78-5

10 Look at the shapes that Jason drew.

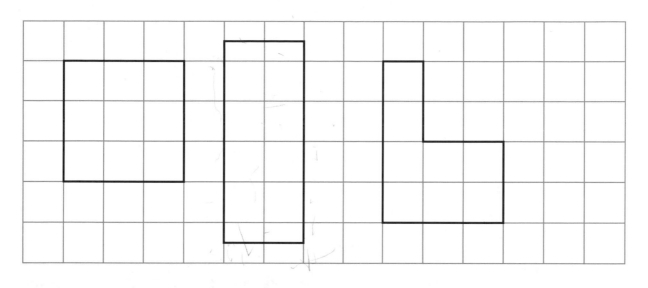

Jason says, "The square has the least perimeter, so it has the least area." Is he correct? If not, what is the correct answer?

Explain Your Thinking

ISBN: 978-1-897164-78-5

1 See how Katie coloured the shape to show a fraction.

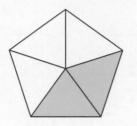

Katie drew and coloured another shape to show the same fraction. Which shape did Katie draw?

○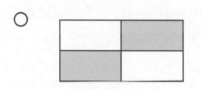

○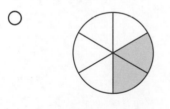

○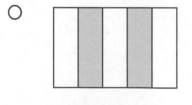

○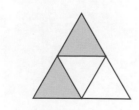

2 Jane caught 135 fish. Eric caught 72 more fish than Jane. If Eric sold 96 of the fish he caught, how many fish would he have left?

○ 111

○ 159

○ 245

○ 303

3 Which number sentence does not belong to the fact family of the addition sentence below?

36 + 28 = 64

○ 28 + 36 = 64

○ 36 − 28 = 8

○ 64 − 36 = 28

○ 64 − 28 = 36

ISBN: 978-1-897164-78-5

4 Uncle Tim draws his hammer on a grid.

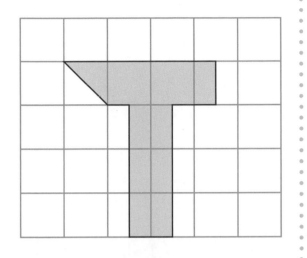

What is the area covered by the hammer in square units?

○ 5

○ 6

○ 7

○ 8

5 Which set of measurements is in order from longest to shortest?

○ 80 cm, 7 m, 900 cm, 20 km

○ 2700 m, 110 m, 18 mm, 2 cm

○ 2800 mm, 1300 mm, 60 m, 20 cm

○ 7 km, 2600 m, 2 km, 300 cm

6 How many vertices are there in a hexagonal pyramid?

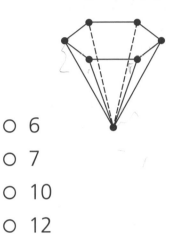

○ 6

○ 7

○ 10

○ 12

7 If half of a watermelon weighs 4 kg, what is the weight of a quarter of the watermelon in kilograms?

○ 2

○ 4

○ 6

○ 8

8 Look at the pattern.

50, ____ , 100, 125, 150

What is the missing number?

○ 60

○ 75

○ 90

○ 110

ISBN: 978-1-897164-78-5

5

9 Put the following fractions in order from least to greatest:

one half, two thirds, three fourths, two fifths

Use the given diagrams to support your answer.

Explain Your Thinking

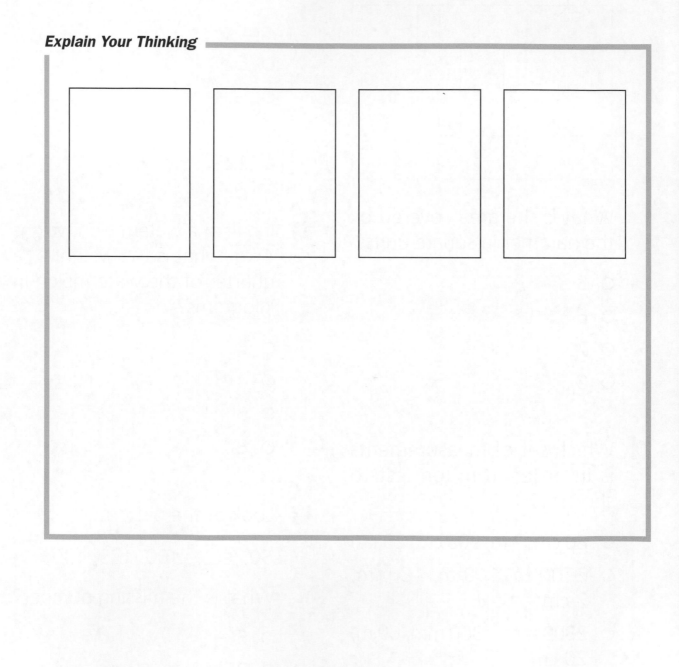

ISBN: 978-1-897164-78-5

10 It takes Danny 45 minutes to finish his dinner every day. The clock below shows the time that Danny finished his dinner today.

What time did Danny start having his dinner?

Explain your answer with the help of the given clock.

Finish Time

Explain Your Thinking

ISBN: 978-1-897164-78-5

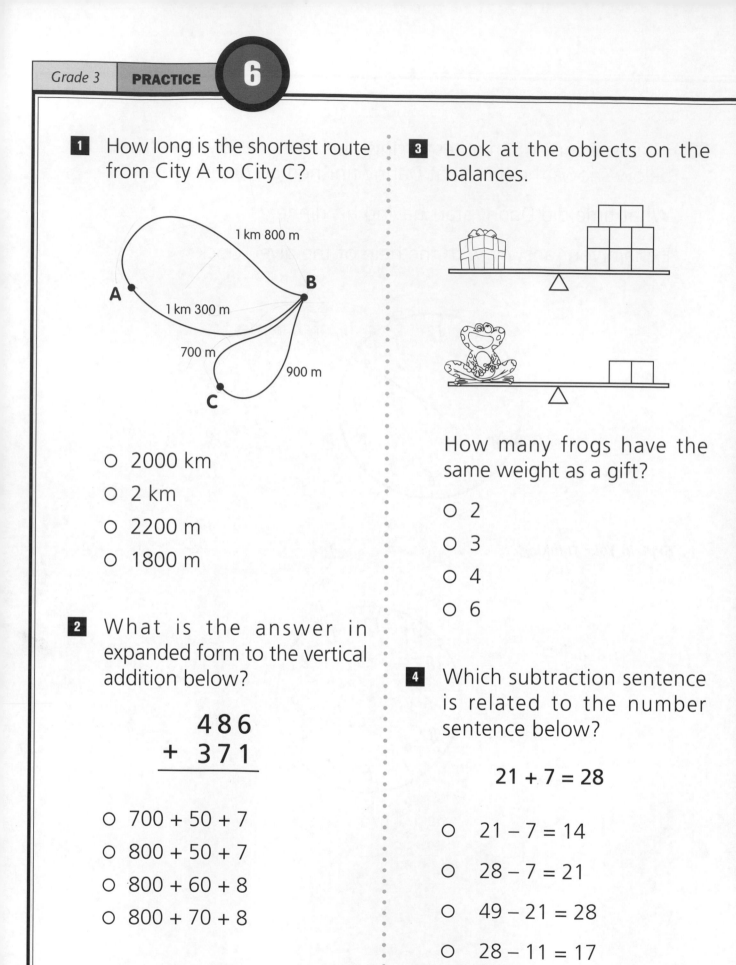

1 How long is the shortest route from City A to City C?

○ 2000 km

○ 2 km

○ 2200 m

○ 1800 m

2 What is the answer in expanded form to the vertical addition below?

$$
\begin{array}{r}
486 \\
+\ 371 \\
\hline
\end{array}
$$

○ 700 + 50 + 7

○ 800 + 50 + 7

○ 800 + 60 + 8

○ 800 + 70 + 8

3 Look at the objects on the balances.

How many frogs have the same weight as a gift?

○ 2

○ 3

○ 4

○ 6

4 Which subtraction sentence is related to the number sentence below?

21 + 7 = 28

○ 21 − 7 = 14

○ 28 − 7 = 21

○ 49 − 21 = 28

○ 28 − 11 = 17

ISBN: 978-1-897164-78-5

5 What transformation does the picture show?

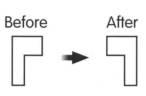

Before   After

- ○ translation
- ○ rotation
- ○ reflection
- ○ translation and rotation

6 The pictograph shows the number of marbles that John has.

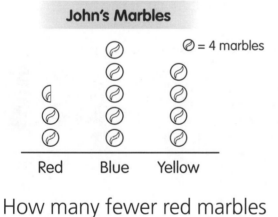

John's Marbles

⊘ = 4 marbles

Red   Blue   Yellow

How many fewer red marbles than blue marbles does John have?

- ○ 10
- ○ 8
- ○ 2
- ○ 12

7 It takes Felix 20 minutes to walk to school. He leaves home at 7:45 a.m. every day. What time does he arrive at school?

- ○ 7:25 a.m.
- ○ 8:05 p.m.
- ○ 8:05 a.m.
- ○ 8:15 a.m.

8 Which line is closest to 4 cm?

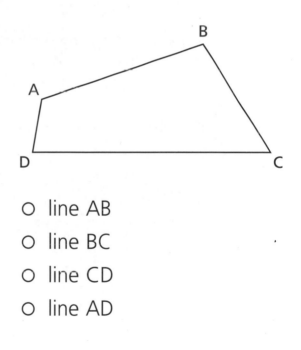

- ○ line AB
- ○ line BC
- ○ line CD
- ○ line AD

 ISBN: 978-1-897164-78-5

9 Jason did a survey on his class about their favourite sports. He used a bar graph to show the data.

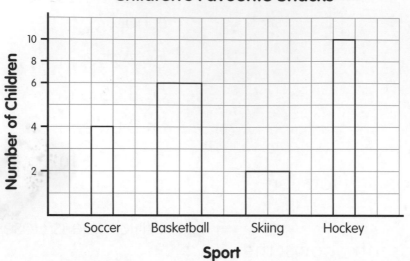

Children's Favourite Snacks

There are 3 mistakes on his graph.

List out the mistakes and draw a correct bar graph.

Show Your Work

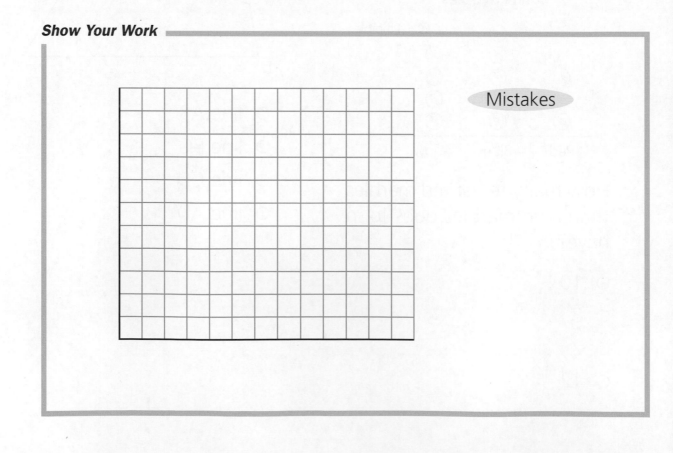

Mistakes

ISBN: 978-1-897164-78-5

10 Annie goes 2 units up and 4 units left to arrive at the library.

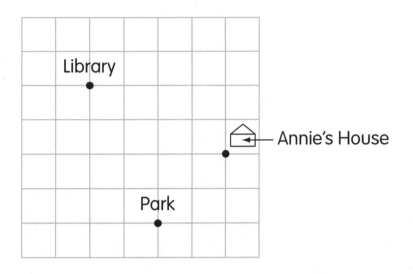

How should Annie go now to get to the park? Then how should Annie go back home from the park?

Show Your Work

ISBN: 978-1-897164-78-5

1 Which sentence about the 3-D figures below is true?

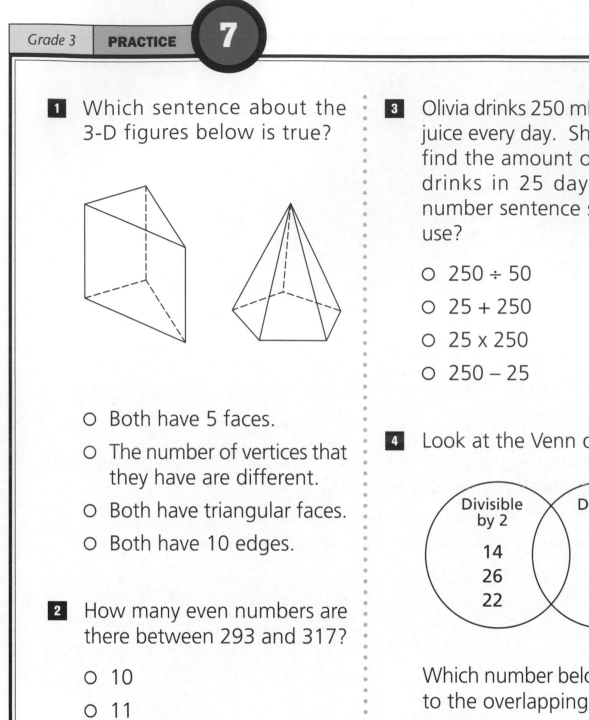

- ○ Both have 5 faces.
- ○ The number of vertices that they have are different.
- ○ Both have triangular faces.
- ○ Both have 10 edges.

2 How many even numbers are there between 293 and 317?

- ○ 10
- ○ 11
- ○ 12
- ○ 13

3 Olivia drinks 250 mL of orange juice every day. She wants to find the amount of juice she drinks in 25 days. Which number sentence should she use?

- ○ 250 ÷ 50
- ○ 25 + 250
- ○ 25 x 250
- ○ 250 – 25

4 Look at the Venn diagram.

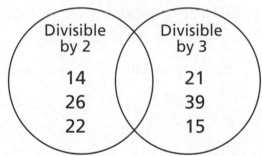

Which number below belongs to the overlapping part?

- ○ 16
- ○ 27
- ○ 42
- ○ 49

ISBN: 978-1-897164-78-5

5 The estimate to the vertical addition below is 500.

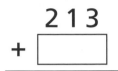

213

+ ☐

Which is the possible missing number?

○ 364

○ 196

○ 283

○ 227

6. Carol spins the spinner at a game fair. She will win a doll if it lands on red.

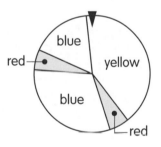

What is the best word to describe the chance that Carol will win a doll?

○ certain

○ unlikely

○ likely

○ impossible

7 Which solid can be formed by the net?

○ hexagonal prism

○ rectangular pyramid

○ pentagonal pyramid

○ hexagonal pyramid

8 How many quarters can trade a toonie?

○ 2

○ 4

○ 8

○ 20

ISBN: 978-1-897164-78-5

9 Jack has 40 bookmarks and Sue has 28.

Jack gives some of his bookmarks to Sue so that they have the same number of bookmarks.

How many bookmarks does Jack give to Sue?

How many bookmarks does each child have now?

Explain Your Thinking

ISBN: 978-1-897164-78-5

10 The map shows where David and Jill live. David needs to follow the direction of the arrows to go to Jill's house from his house.

List out all the possible routes that David can take. Then find the distance of taking each route.

What do you notice from the answer?

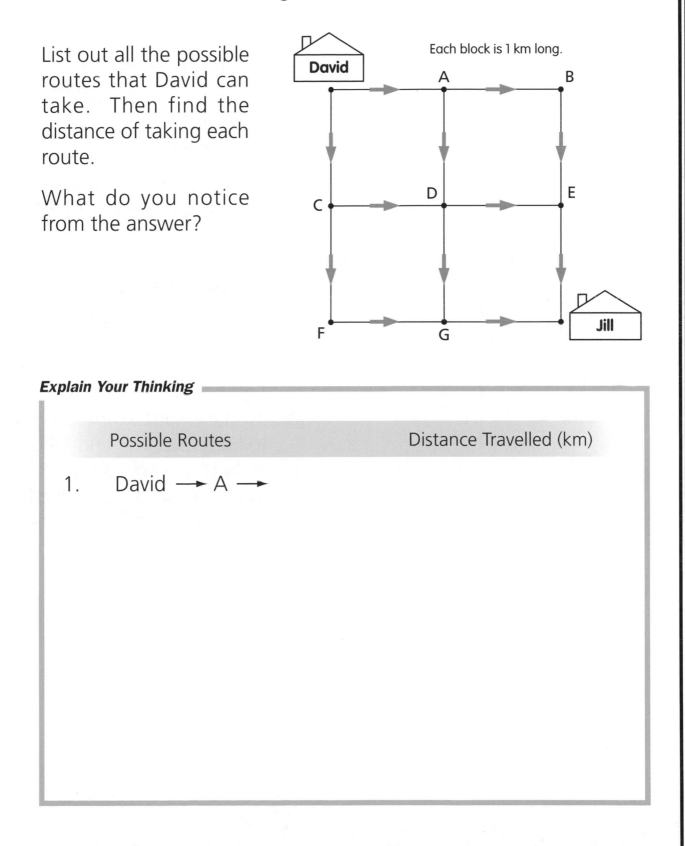

Each block is 1 km long.

Explain Your Thinking

Possible Routes	Distance Travelled (km)
1. David ⟶ A ⟶	

ISBN: 978-1-897164-78-5

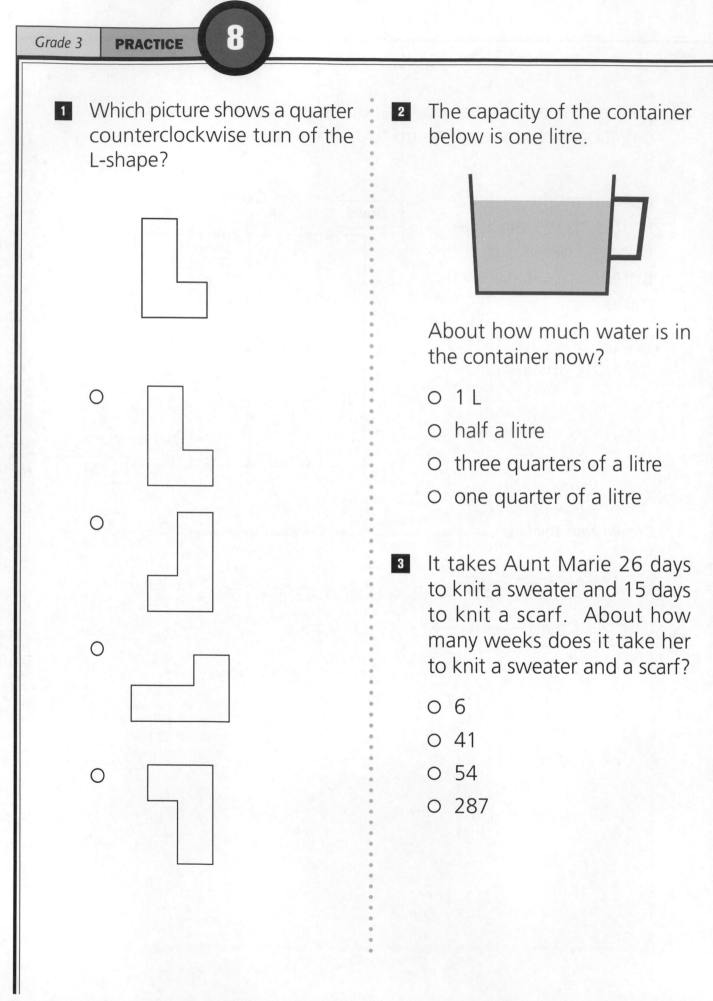

1 Which picture shows a quarter counterclockwise turn of the L-shape?

○

○

○

○

2 The capacity of the container below is one litre.

About how much water is in the container now?

○ 1 L

○ half a litre

○ three quarters of a litre

○ one quarter of a litre

3 It takes Aunt Marie 26 days to knit a sweater and 15 days to knit a scarf. About how many weeks does it take her to knit a sweater and a scarf?

○ 6

○ 41

○ 54

○ 287

ISBN: 978-1-897164-78-5

4 What is the perimeter of a regular octagon with a side length of 5 cm?

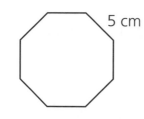

5 cm

- ○ 8 cm
- ○ 25 cm
- ○ 30 cm
- ○ 40 cm

5 How can ☆ be moved to ☾ on the grid?

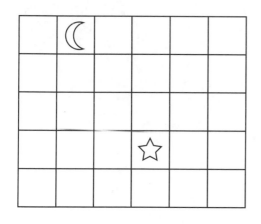

- ○ 2 units left, 3 units up
- ○ 3 units left, 2 units up
- ○ 2 units right, 3 units down
- ○ 3 units right, 2 units down

6 The graph shows the number of storybooks the children have read.

No. of Storybooks Read

☐ = 4 books

Joe   Mark   Sue   May

How many storybooks have the girls read in all?

- ○ 6
- ○ 9
- ○ 12
- ○ 16

7 Bob started working on his project on May 16, 2006 and finished it on June 2, 2007. How long did it take Bob to finish his project?

- ○ about 1 week
- ○ about 2 weeks
- ○ about 1 year
- ○ about 2 years

ISBN: 978-1-897164-78-5

8 Look at Linda's number pattern.

Linda's number pattern: **3, 7, 6, 10, 9, 13**

Make two number patterns using Linda's pattern rule:

1. Start with "1" and write the next 5 terms.

2. Start with your own number and write the next 4 terms.

Show Your Work

ISBN: 978-1-897164-78-5

9 Aunt Katie wants to build a rectangular flower bed which has an area of 6 square units.

Find two possible ways of building the flower bed. Draw them on the grid.

If Aunt Katie wants to use less fencing for the flower bed, which dimensions should she choose?

1 square unit

Explain Your Thinking

ISBN: 978-1-897164-78-5

1 Which solid is described by the sentences below?

- It has 5 vertices.
- It has 5 faces.
- It has 4 triangular faces.
- It has 1 rectangular face.

O triangular prism

O rectangular pyramid

O rectangular prism

O pentagonal prism

2 Tony is tossing a cube that is labelled 1 to 6 on each face. What is the probability that he will get a 3 or 4?

O 1 in 6

O 2 in 6

O 4 in 6

O 6 in 6

3 What fraction of the square is not shaded?

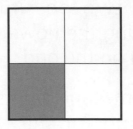

O one half

O one fourth

O three thirds

O three fourths

4 What is the area of the shape below in square units?

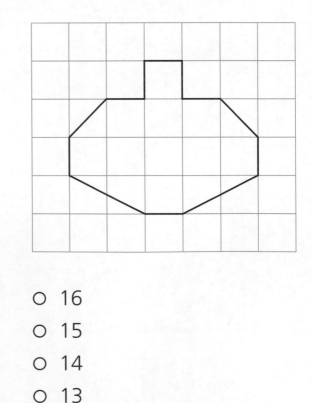

O 16

O 15

O 14

O 13

ISBN: 978-1-897164-78-5

5 The graph shows the number of ice cream cones sold yesterday.

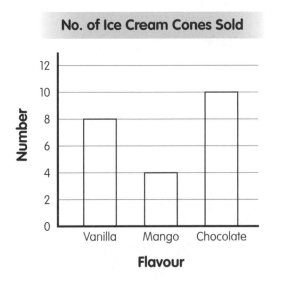

No. of Ice Cream Cones Sold

How many ice cream cones were sold yesterday?

○ 9

○ 11

○ 18

○ 22

6 What is the time elapsed from 7:55 p.m. to 8:35 p.m.?

○ 30 minutes

○ 40 minutes

○ 1 hour 20 minutes

○ 1 hour 40 minutes

7 Janet measured and wrote, "My book is 25 thick." Which measuring unit is missing from the sentence?

○ millimetres

○ centimetres

○ metres

○ kilometres

8 Each box has 5 crayons and 2 of them are red. How many red crayons are there in 6 boxes?

○ 10

○ 12

○ 24

○ 30

9 Which of the following is best to describe 33 days?

○ about 1 week

○ about 1 month

○ about 3 months

○ about 1 year

ISBN: 978-1-897164-78-5

9

10 Mrs. Green bought 12 eggs. Unfortunately, one third of the eggs were broken. Mrs. Green used one fourth of the remaining eggs to make cookies.

How many eggs does Mrs. Green have left?

Show your work with the help of pictures.

Explain Your Thinking

ISBN: 978-1-897164-78-5

11 Janet is drawing symmetrical nets for a 3-D figure.

Help her complete the nets and tell what figure the nets can form.

Show Your Work

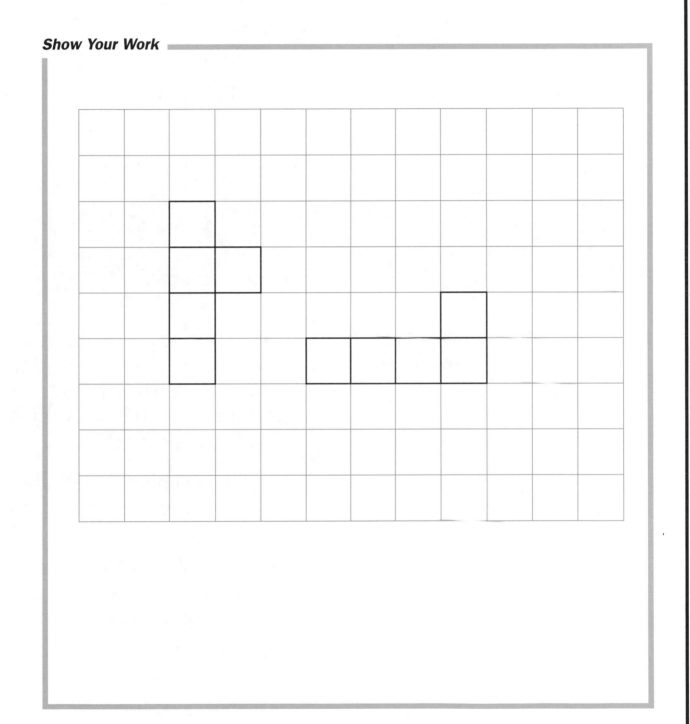

ISBN: 978-1-897164-78-5

1 How many line(s) of symmetry does the hexagon have?

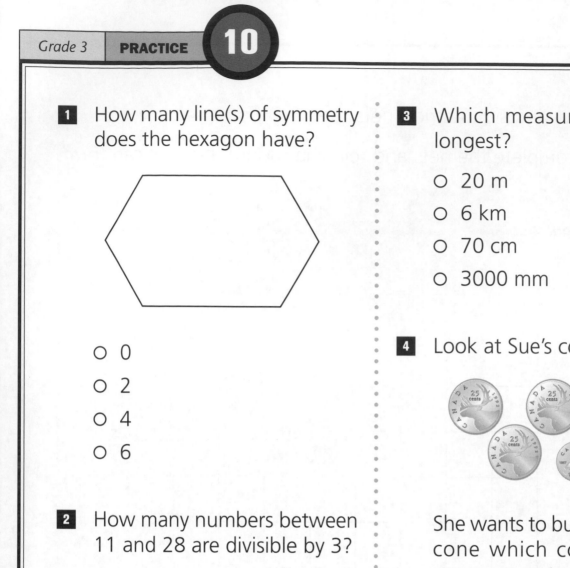

- ○ 0
- ○ 2
- ○ 4
- ○ 6

2 How many numbers between 11 and 28 are divisible by 3?

- ○ 3
- ○ 4
- ○ 5
- ○ 6

3 Which measurement is the longest?

- ○ 20 m
- ○ 6 km
- ○ 70 cm
- ○ 3000 mm

4 Look at Sue's coins.

She wants to buy an ice cream cone which costs 85¢ and pays an extra of 25¢ for adding sprinkles. Which sentence is correct?

- ○ She will have 5¢ left after buying an ice cream cone with sprinkles.
- ○ She will have 10¢ left after buying an ice cream cone with sprinkles.
- ○ She needs 5¢ more to get what she wants.
- ○ She needs 10¢ more to get what she wants.

ISBN: 978-1-897164-78-5

5 6 ⬜ fill a 🍺 .

4 🫗 fill a 🪣 .

How many ⬜ are needed to fill a 🪣 ?

- ○ 4
- ○ 6
- ○ 24
- ○ 36

6 What number does A represent?

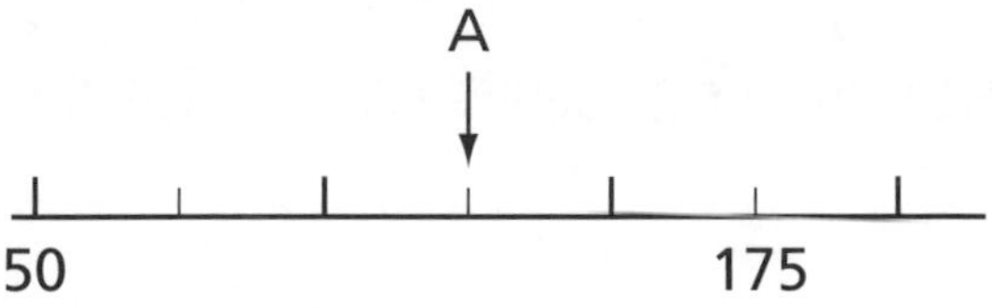

50   175

- ○ 75
- ○ 125
- ○ 150
- ○ 200

7 Look at the pattern.

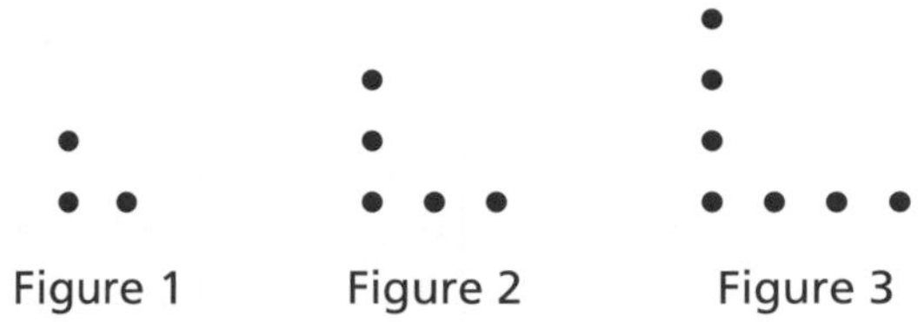

Figure 1   Figure 2   Figure 3

How many dots will there be in Figure 6?

- ○ 9
- ○ 11
- ○ 13
- ○ 15

8 The net below makes a rectangular prism.

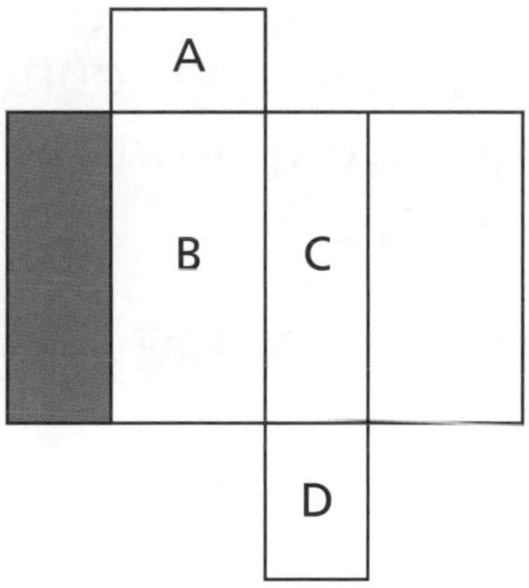

Which face is opposite to the shaded one?

- ○ A
- ○ B
- ○ C
- ○ D

ISBN: 978-1-897164-78-5

9 Circle 38 on the hundreds chart.

1	2	3	4	5	6	7	8	9	10
11	12	13	14	15	16	17	18	19	20
21	22	23	24	25	26	27	28	29	30
31	32	33	34	35	36	37	38	39	40
41	42	43	44	45	46	47	48	49	50
51	52	53	54	55	56	57	58	59	60
61	62	63	64	65	66	67	68	69	70
71	72	73	74	75	76	77	78	79	80
81	82	83	84	85	86	87	88	89	90
91	92	93	94	95	96	97	98	99	100

Start at 38 and count on by 9's six times. Circle the numbers that you have got on the chart. Describe the pattern of the circled numbers.

Explain Your Thinking

ISBN: 978-1-897164-78-5

10 Look at the objects below.

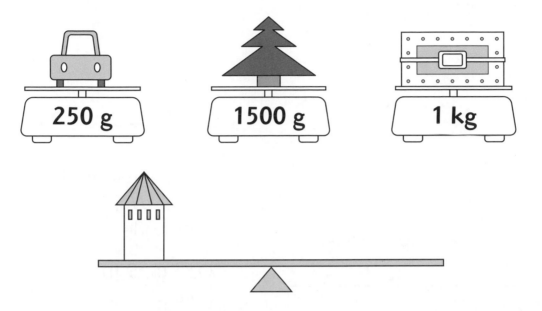

The tower weighs 2 kg. Show 2 different ways to balance the tower using the objects above. You can use each object more than once.

Show your answer with drawings.

Explain Your Thinking

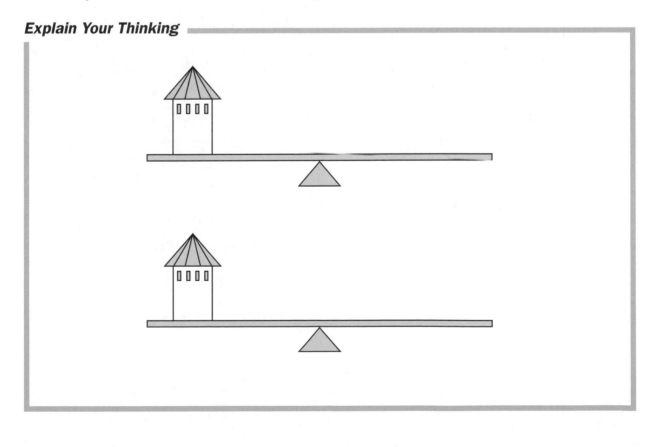

ISBN: 978-1-897164-78-5

1 Each pizza is cut into 8 slices. How many slices are there in 3 pizzas?

- ○ 16
- ○ 24
- ○ 28
- ○ 32

2 Look at the shapes below.

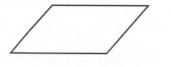

Which sentence about the shapes is false?

- ○ They have two pairs of equal sides.
- ○ They have two pairs of parallel sides.
- ○ They are quadrilaterals.
- ○ They have exactly one pair of equal angles.

3 Look at the shape below.

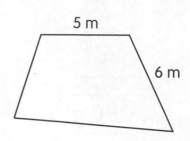

The perimeter of the shape is 25 m. Which set might be the missing lengths?

- ○ 5 m, 9 m
- ○ 6 m, 7 m
- ○ 7 m, 8 m
- ○ 14 m, 14 m

4 Look at the pattern.

$$1 + 7 = 8$$
$$2 + 6 = 8$$
$$3 + 5 = 8$$

Which number sentence comes next?

- ○ 5 + 3 = 8
- ○ 4 + 4 = 8
- ○ 8 + 3 = 11
- ○ 8 − 5 = 3

ISBN: 978-1-897164-78-5

5 Look at the diagram.

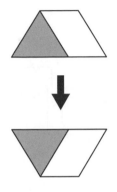

What transformation does it show?

○ rotation

○ reflection

○ circulation

○ translation

6 A can fill 4 . Each can hold 250 mL of water.

What is the capacity of a ?

○ 500 mL

○ 1 L

○ 1000 L

○ 2000 mL

7 Mrs. Karr gives an assignment to her class on June 22 and says, "This assignment is due in 2 weeks." On what date is the assignment due?

June						
S	M	T	W	T	F	S
					1	2
3	4	5	6	7	8	9
10	11	12	13	14	15	16
17	18	19	20	21	22	23
24	25	26	27	28	29	30

○ June 8

○ June 15

○ July 5

○ July 6

8 Celine paid $5 for a sandwich which cost $3.35. The cashier gave her the change with the fewest coins. How many coins were there?

○ 2

○ 3

○ 5

○ 7

ISBN: 978-1-897164-78-5

9 Janet has 6 cards each labelled "1", "2", and "3". She shuffles the cards and draws one card each time.

Look at the results of her 30 draws.

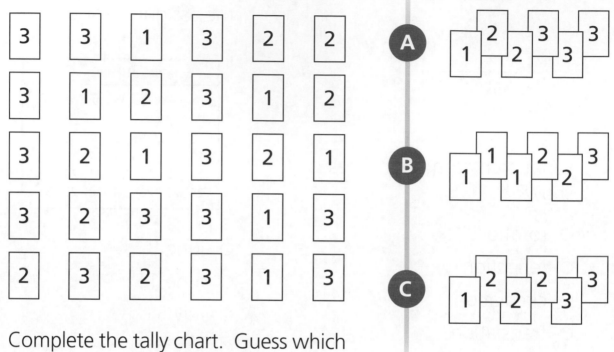

Complete the tally chart. Guess which set of cards Janet might have.

Explain your choice.

Explain Your Thinking

Card Number	Tally
1	
2	
3	

ISBN: 978-1-897164-78-5

10 Pizza A was cut into 8 equal slices and Pizza B was cut into 6 equal slices.

Uncle Sam ate 5 slices of Pizza A.

Uncle Tom ate 4 slices of Pizza B.

Uncle Sam says, "I've eaten more pizza than Tom."

Is he correct? Complete and label the diagrams to help explain your thinking.

Explain Your Thinking

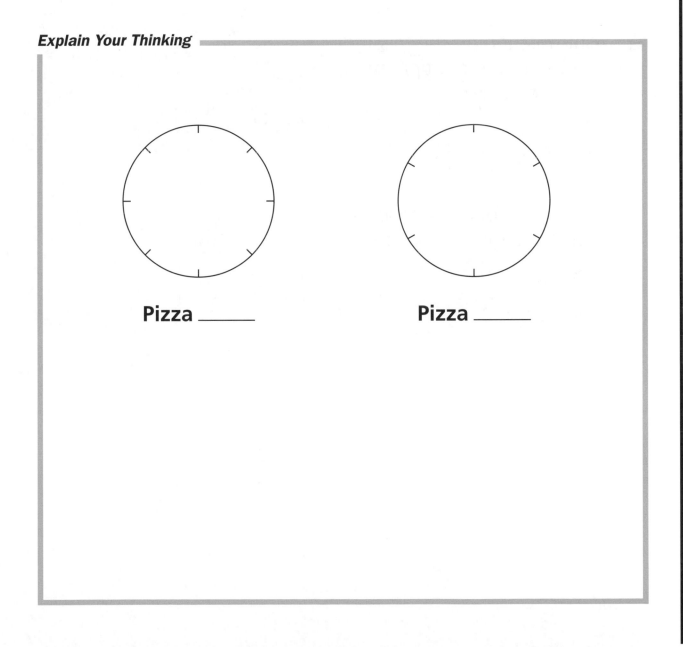

Pizza _____   **Pizza** _____

ISBN: 978-1-897164-78-5

1 Tom's mother gives Tom $3 every week. How long will it take Tom to save $12 if he spends $1 a week?

○ 4 weeks

○ 6 weeks

○ 10 days

○ 12 days

2 Ashley is finding the missing number in the multiplication sentence below.

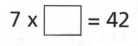

$$7 \times \boxed{} = 42$$

Which related fact can she use to find the missing number?

○ 42 ÷ 6 = 7

○ 42 − 7 = 35

○ 7 + 35 = 42

○ 42 × 7 = 294

3 Kevin has a bag of 20 apples. 5 of them are golden, 3 are green, and the rest are red. What fraction of the apples is red?

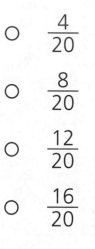

○ $\dfrac{4}{20}$

○ $\dfrac{8}{20}$

○ $\dfrac{12}{20}$

○ $\dfrac{16}{20}$

4 Ann shares 24 marbles equally with 2 friends. How many marbles does each child get?

○ 3

○ 4

○ 8

○ 12

ISBN: 978-1-897164-78-5

5 What fraction of the circle is shaded?

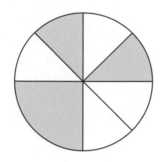

○ $\dfrac{3}{7}$

○ $\dfrac{3}{4}$

○ $\dfrac{3}{8}$

○ $\dfrac{4}{8}$

6 Cathy wants to paint all the triangular faces of the triangular prism.

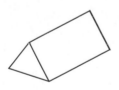

How many faces will be painted?

○ 2

○ 3

○ 4

○ 5

7 What is the best word to describe the chance of drawing a ⊛ or ◎ from the box below?

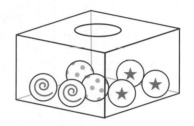

○ impossible

○ unlikely

○ likely

○ certain

8 The number of vertices that a pentagonal prism has is 2 times that of a rectangular pyramid.

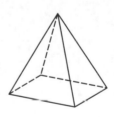

How many vertices does a pentagonal prism have?

○ 5

○ 7

○ 10

○ 12

ISBN: 978-1-897164-78-5

9 Tom walks his dog around a rectangular park.

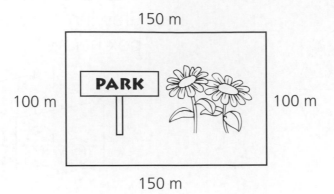

150 m

100 m   100 m

150 m

If Tom and his dog walk around the park 3 times, what will be the total distance travelled?

Explain Your Thinking

ISBN: 978-1-897164-78-5

10 Mrs. Pitt decorates a wall with a trim of shapes. Each unit of her design contains 2 triangles and 3 circles.

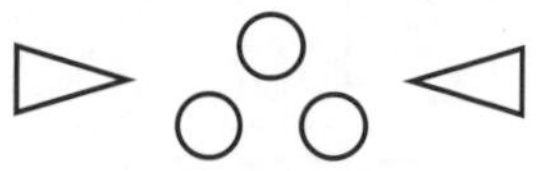

Record the number of each kind of shape in the first four units in the chart.

Following the pattern, how many units can Mrs. Pitt make with 12 triangles?

How many circles are needed to go with 12 triangles?

Explain Your Thinking

Units	Triangles	Circles

ISBN: 978-1-897164-78-5

1 Draw a card without looking.

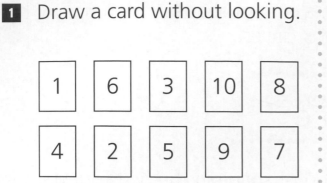

Which sentence describes the chance of drawing an even number card and the chance of drawing an odd number card?

○ There is a better chance of drawing an odd number card.

○ It is equally likely to draw an odd number card or an even number card.

○ There is a better chance of drawing an even number card.

○ It is certain to draw an odd number card and impossible to draw an even number card.

2 Count the number of faces on each figure.

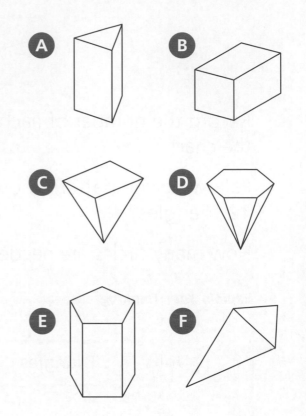

Which set contains the figures that have more than 5 faces?

○ A, C, and F

○ B, C, and F

○ A, C, and E

○ B, D, and E

ISBN: 978-1-897164-78-5

3 Which of the following is another way to show 3 x 5?

- ○ 5 x 5 x 5
- ○ 3 + 3 + 3
- ○ 5 + 5 + 5
- ○ 3 x 3 x 3

4 Bill has 127 $10 bills, and Connie has 13 fewer $10 bills than Bill does. How many $10 bills does Connie have?

- ○ 114
- ○ 140
- ○ 170
- ○ 1140

5 Look at the number pattern.

4, 7, 6, 9, 8, 11,...

What is the pattern rule?

- ○ add 1, subtract 3
- ○ subtract 3, add 1
- ○ add 3, subtract 1
- ○ add 3, subtract 3

6 Which object is in the shape of a cylinder?

- ○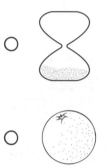
- ○
- ○
- ○ (ice cream cone)

7 The opposite sides of a rectangle are equal in length.

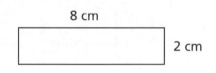

What is the perimeter of the rectangle?

- ○ 10 cm
- ○ 16 cm
- ○ 18 cm
- ○ 20 cm

ISBN: 978-1-897164-78-5

13

8 The T-shirts in Uncle Sam's Store are in 4 different colours. There are 100 T-shirts in each colour. Below is the number of T-shirts in stock after a week.

	Red	Blue	Orange	Green
No. of T-Shirts in Stock	26	35	19	52

If Uncle Sam orders more T-shirts for next week, should he order the same number of T-shirts of each colour? If not, which colour should he order the most?

Round the data to the nearest ten and draw a horizontal bar graph using the rounded data.

Explain Your Thinking

	Red	Blue	Orange	Green
Rounded Numbers				

ISBN: 978-1-897164-78-5

9 Follow the rules and sort the numbers in the box into the Venn diagram.

Explain how you sorted the numbers into the overlapping part. Then give one more example in each part of the diagram. Write the example in the circle.

10	15
35	16
20	12
8	40

Explain Your Thinking

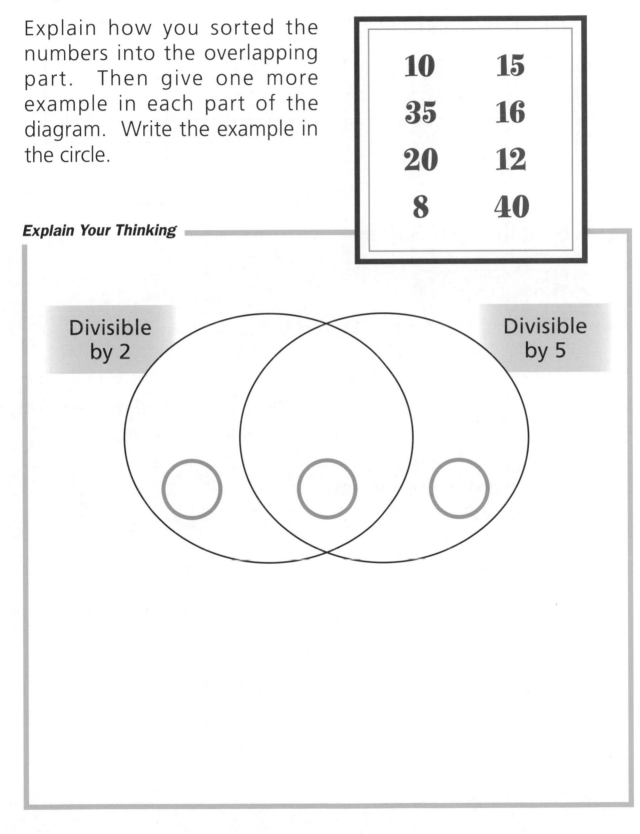

Divisible by 2

Divisible by 5

ISBN: 978-1-897164-78-5

1 Which number pattern has the pattern rule below?

"Multiply by 2 and add 1."

○ 4, 8, 12, 16, 20

○ 1, 4, 10, 22, 46

○ 2, 5, 11, 23, 47

○ 3, 5, 9, 17, 33

2 Look at the Venn Diagram.

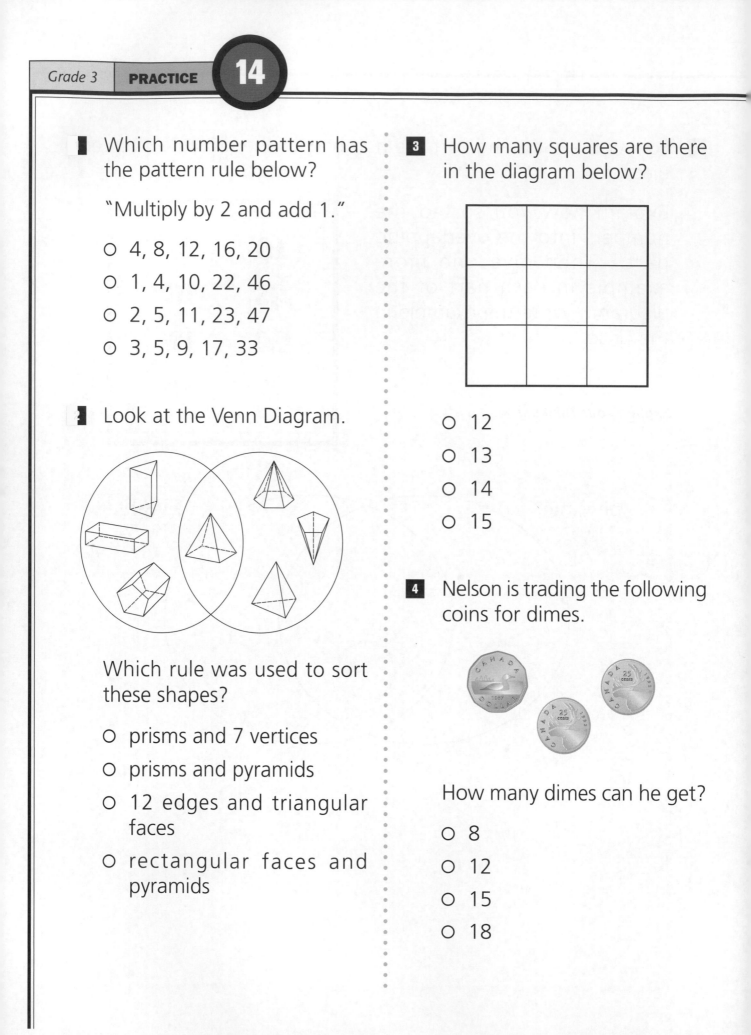

Which rule was used to sort these shapes?

○ prisms and 7 vertices

○ prisms and pyramids

○ 12 edges and triangular faces

○ rectangular faces and pyramids

3 How many squares are there in the diagram below?

○ 12

○ 13

○ 14

○ 15

4 Nelson is trading the following coins for dimes.

How many dimes can he get?

○ 8

○ 12

○ 15

○ 18

ISBN: 978-1-897164-78-5

5 It is 11:45 a.m. now. What time will it be after 35 minutes?

○ 12:35 p.m.

○ 12:00 p.m.

○ 12:20 p.m.

○ 11:20 a.m.

6 Vincent made the pattern below with arrows.

↑ ← ↓ → ↑ ←

Which sentence best describes the pattern rule?

○ The arrow points up and then points to the left.

○ The arrow points down each time.

○ The arrow makes a $\frac{1}{4}$ counterclockwise turn each time.

○ The arrow flips vertically each time.

7 Which of the following could be the temperature of the lemonade in degrees Celsius?

○ 45

○ 37

○ 24

○ 4

8 Joseph has 35 cookies. If he puts his cookies equally into 7 boxes, how many cookies are there in each box?

○ 7

○ 49

○ 5

○ 35

ISBN: 978-1-897164-78-5

9 Mrs. Thompson bought 1 bag of chips on Sunday, 2 bags on Monday, 3 bags on Tuesday, and 4 bags on Wednesday.

If she follows this pattern to buy chips, how many bags of chips will she buy on Thursday, Friday, and Saturday?

How many bags of chips will she buy in a week?

Explain Your Thinking

ISBN: 978-1-897164-78-5

10 The children are going to spin the spinner below 60 times. Each child has made a prediction on the result.

Children	No. of Times		
	Red	Green	Blue
Lisa	32	19	9
Brian	14	16	30
Cindy	12	19	29

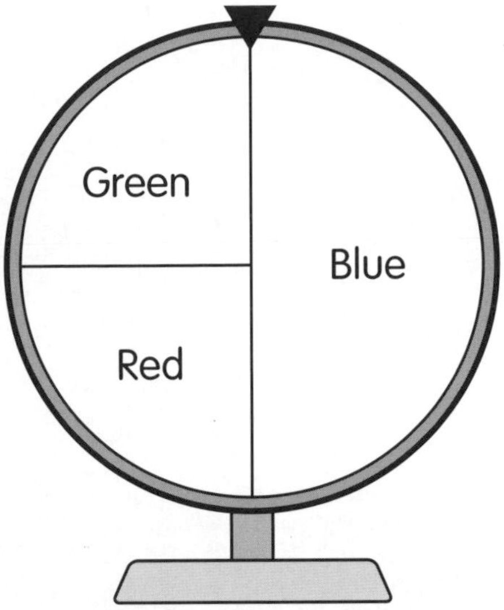

Green

Blue

Red

Who has made the most reasonable prediction?

Explain Your Thinking

ISBN: 978-1-897164-78-5

Assessment of
MATHEMATICS

Grade
3

 ISBN: 978-1-897164-78-5

1 There are 126 red balls, 214 green balls, and 98 balls in other colours in a box. How many balls are there in the box?

- ○ 186
- ○ 214
- ○ 242
- ○ 438

2 Which is the best estimate of the sum of the addition below?

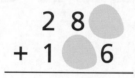

$$\begin{array}{r} 2\ 8\ \bullet \\ +\ 1\ \bullet\ 6 \\ \hline \end{array}$$

- ○ between 400 and 500
- ○ close to 500
- ○ less than 400
- ○ greater than 500

3 What number does the arrow point at on the number line below?

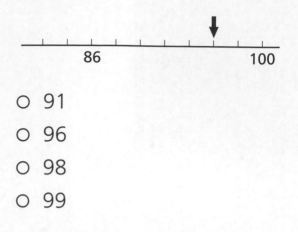

- ○ 91
- ○ 96
- ○ 98
- ○ 99

4 Lucy is making a gift box with the net below.

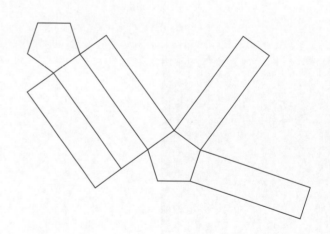

What is the figure of the gift box?

- ○ rectangular prism
- ○ pentagonal prism
- ○ rectangular pyramid
- ○ pentagonal pyramid

ISBN: 978-1-897164-78-5

5 Julia has made a number pattern – add and then subtract. Which of the following could be Julia's pattern?

○ 13, 14, 16, 19, 23

○ 17, 20, 19, 22, 21

○ 20, 40, 60, 80, 100

○ 31, 26, 21, 16, 11

6 Look at the coins that Jason has.

If he pays the exact amount for a lollipop that costs $1.26 with the fewest coins, which coins will he have left?

○ 1 dime and 3 nickels

○ 1 quarter and 1 penny

○ 1 loonie and 1 penny

○ 1 quarter and 2 nickels

7 Kelvin is going to spin the spinner once.

What is the probability that he will win a prize?

○ 2 out of 4

○ 2 out of 6

○ 6 out of 2

○ 4 out of 6

8 Tony is measuring his hand span. Which of the following could be the measurement of his hand span?

○ 13 mm

○ 11 m

○ 12 cm

○ 15 km

ISBN: 978-1-897164-78-5

9 The flag is moved from M to N as shown on the grid below.

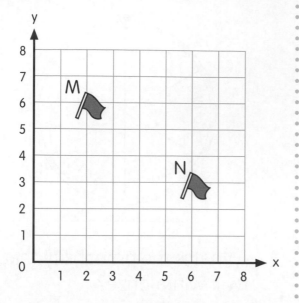

Which of the following describes the translation of the flag correctly?

○ 4 units left, then 3 units up

○ 3 units left, then 4 units up

○ 3 units right, then 4 units down

○ 4 units right, then 3 units down

10 Which subtraction sentence is related to 27 + 12 = 39?

○ 39 – 17 = 22

○ 39 – 12 = 27

○ 51 – 12 = 39

○ 27 – 12 = 15

11 Look at the points that Christine got in the first two rounds of a game.

Round	Score (points)
1st	124
2nd	98
3rd	

The score that Christine got in the 3rd round is 103 points fewer than the total score of the first two rounds. How many points did she get in the 3rd round?

○ 77

○ 119

○ 129

○ 325

12 It takes Sarah 69 days to make a doll. About how many weeks does it take her to make a doll?

○ 3

○ 6

○ 8

○ 10

ISBN: 978-1-897164-78-5

13 Which of the following could be the temperature of a freezer?

○ 3°C

○ 36°C

○ −11°C

○ 98°C

14 The graph below shows the number of servings of fruit that each child eats in a week.

No. of Servings of Fruit that Each Child Eats in a Week

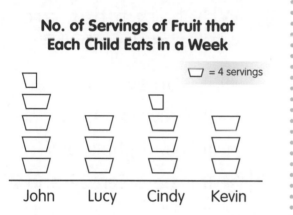

⬱ = 4 servings

John   Lucy   Cindy   Kevin

How many more servings of fruit do the boys have than the girls?

○ 1

○ 2

○ 4

○ 6

15 Which of the following sentence is true about a rectangular pyramid?

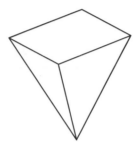

○ It has 5 edges.

○ It has 5 rectangular faces.

○ It has 8 vertices.

○ It has 4 triangular faces.

16 What is the missing number in the pattern below?

_____ , 30, 46, 62, 78

○ 46

○ 26

○ 14

○ 12

ISBN: 978-1-897164-78-5

17 Bernice has poured water into some glasses.

What fraction of the glasses is filled with water?

- ○ $\frac{2}{3}$
- ○ $\frac{2}{5}$
- ○ $\frac{3}{5}$
- ○ $\frac{4}{5}$

18 Michael wants to find the perimeter of a regular pentagon with a side length of 6 cm. Which number sentence should he use?

- ○ 5 x 5 x 5 x 5
- ○ 6 x 6 x 6 x 6 x 6
- ○ 5 + 5 + 5 + 5 + 5
- ○ 6 + 6 + 6 + 6 + 6

19 Which of the following slots is 248?

240   256

- ○ A
- ○ B
- ○ C
- ○ D

20 Which number are the sentences describing?

- It is an even number.
- It is divisible by 4.
- It is a multiple of 7.
- It is between 22 and 53.

- ○ 12
- ○ 28
- ○ 49
- ○ 56

ISBN: 978-1-897164-78-5

21 Omar shares 42 gumballs equally with 6 of his cousins. How many gumballs does each person get?

○ 6

○ 7

○ 12

○ 14

22 The chart below shows the number of cans a family collected last week.

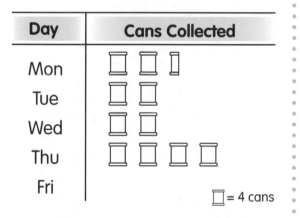

The number of cans collected on Friday doubled the number collected on Monday. How many cans should be drawn to complete the chart?

○ 2

○ 5

○ 10

○ 12

23 How many lines of symmetry are there in the shape below?

○ 2

○ 4

○ 6

○ 8

24 Daisy and Leo are building towers with blocks. The first tower is 2 blocks high, the second is 5 blocks high, the third is 8 blocks high and so on. How high will be the 7th tower?

○ 13

○ 15

○ 20

○ 23

ISBN: 978-1-897164-78-5

25 Which of the following is the best measurement of the weight of a watermelon?

- ○ 200 g
- ○ 5 L
- ○ 6 kg
- ○ 3000 mL

26 Justin and Kelsey started their journey at 7:05 p.m. Justin arrived at the destination at 7:43 p.m. and Kelsey arrived 14 minutes later. What time did Kelsey arrive at the destination?

- ○ 7:19 p.m.
- ○ 7:29 p.m.
- ○ 7:57 p.m.
- ○ 8:14 p.m.

27 Look at Peter's design.

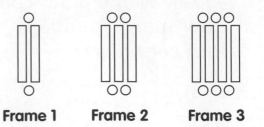

Frame 1   **Frame 2**   **Frame 3**

How many circles are there in the frame that has 6 rectangles?

- ○ 8
- ○ 10
- ○ 12
- ○ 14

28 How many nickels have the same value as the coins shown below?

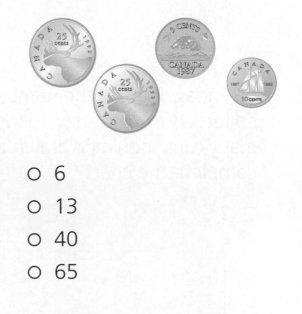

- ○ 6
- ○ 13
- ○ 40
- ○ 65

ISBN: 978-1-897164-78-5

29 Mr. Green is drawing squares to make frames on his driveway using chalks. The number of squares and perimeter of each frame are recorded below.

Frame	Perimeter (Units)
	4
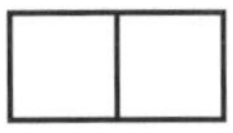	6
	8
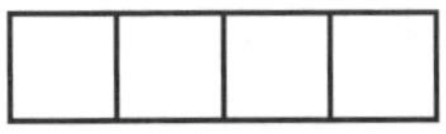	10

What is the pattern rule for the perimeters?

If Mr. Green puts 5 pebbles in each square, what is the perimeter of the frame that has a total of 25 pebbles in it?

Explain Your Thinking

ISBN: 978-1-897164-78-5

30 Sandra says, "I can build one prism and one pyramid with 6 pieces of modelling clay for each."

Do you think what Sandra says is possible?

Draw the figures to support your answer. Then describe the figures in terms of their edges and faces.

Show Your Work

ISBN: 978-1-897164-78-5

31 Jill did a survey on the number of hours her 22 friends spent watching TV in a week. She recorded the results in a tally chart.

Unfortunately, her cat tore a corner away.

Jill says, "I cannot make a bar graph to show the data anymore because there is some information missing."

Do you agree with Jill?

If not, explain and use the data to make a bar graph.

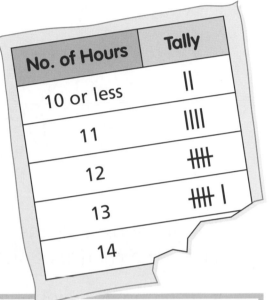

No. of Hours	Tally
10 or less	II
11	IIII
12	HH
13	HH I
14	

Explain Your Thinking

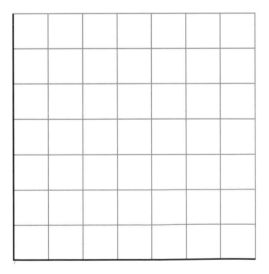

ISBN: 978-1-897164-78-5

32 Carmen put 10 balls into the box and asked George to draw one without looking.

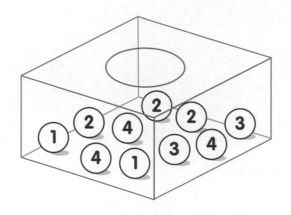

Carmen looked at the number on the ball that George drew and said, "The chance of drawing this ball is 3 out of 10."

Which number might be on the ball?

Explain Your Thinking

ISBN: 978-1-897164-78-5

33 Steven and his sister want to buy a storybook which costs $8 for their brother.

The coins that each child has are as follows:

Steven: 4 loonies, 3 dimes, and 4 pennies

His sister: 2 toonies, 3 quarters, 4 dimes, and 3 nickels

If they chip in, will they be able to buy the storybook?

Explain Your Thinking

ISBN: 978-1-897164-78-5

34 The areas of figure A and figure B are the same.

Jenny thinks that the perimeters of these two figures are the same too.

Do you agree? Give reasons to support your thinking.

Explain Your Thinking

ISBN: 978-1-897164-78-5

35 Annie is making necklaces with red and blue beads. There are 9 beads on each necklace. The number of red beads on each necklace is 1 more than the blue ones.

How many red beads does she need to make 8 necklaces?

Show Your Work

ISBN: 978-1-897164-78-5

36 You are treasure hunting.

What is the shortest and safest path to collect all the keys to the treasure chest?

You can move vertically or horizontally only.

You are here.

Show Your Work

ISBN: 978-1-897164-78-5

Practice 1

1. 14
2. C
3. a bit shorter than 7 cm
4. rectangular prism
5. 7:15
6. 340 – 290
7. 16
8. unlikely
9. No. Andy has 28 stickers and Linda has 50. Linda has more stickers than Andy.

10

Number of Apples	Number of Customers
1 – 5	IIII
6 – 10	IIII
11 – 15	IIII III
16 – 20	IIII
21 – 25	II

Most customers buy 11 – 15 apples.

Practice 2

1. 6:50 p.m.
2. 31 + 27 = 58
3. 429
4. rectangular pyramid
5. 7
6. 2
7. 88, 92
8. 398
9.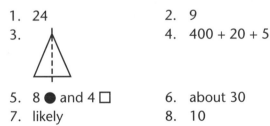

Each of the 3 helpers takes care of 5 children and 1 helper takes care of 2. Mrs. Smith needs 4 helpers.
10. Andrew misplaced the rectangular pyramid because it has 5 vertices instead of 6.

Practice 3

1. 24
2. 9
3.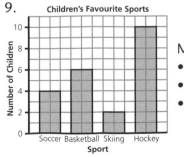
4. 400 + 20 + 5
5. 8 ● and 4 ◻
6. about 30
7. likely
8. 10
9. I would use Way 1 because it is unlikely to draw a red ball, the prize of which costs the most, and it is most likely to draw a black ball, the prize of which costs least.
10. He will have the following coins left:

($2) (5¢) (5¢) (5¢) (5¢) (1¢) (1¢) (1¢)

1 toonie, 4 nickels, and 3 pennies
The total value is 2 dollars and 23 cents.

Practice 4

1. 20 cm
2.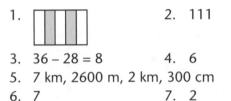
3. 5:20
4. a quarter
5. 629
6. 10
7. 24
8. 213
9. She bought a total of 36 lollipops. There are 9 lollipops in each bag.
10. Perimeter (units):
square: 12 ; rectangle: 14 ; L-shape: 14
Area (square units):
square: 9 ; rectangle: 10 ; L-shape: 8
He is not correct. The L-shape has the least area.

Practice 5

1. [grid figure]
2. 111
3. 36 – 28 = 8
4. 6
5. 7 km, 2600 m, 2 km, 300 cm
6. 7
7. 2
8. 75
9.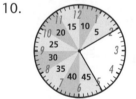

one half   two thirds   three fourths   two fifths

Least to greatest:
two fifths, one half, two thirds, three fourths
10.

We can count 45 minutes backward to find the time that Danny started his dinner. The time was 6:25.

Practice 6

1. 2 km
2. 800 + 50 + 7
3. 4
4. 28 – 7 = 21
5. reflection
6. 10
7. 8:05 a.m.
8. line AB
9.
Children's Favourite Sports

[bar graph: y-axis "Number of Children" 0 to 10; x-axis "Sport" with Soccer (4), Basketball (6), Skiing (2), Hockey (10)]

Mistakes:
• wrong title
• uneven scale
• uneven width of the bars

ISBN: 978-1-897164-78-5

10. Annie should go 2 units right and 4 units down to get to the park. Then 2 units right and 2 units up to go back home.

Practice 7

1. Both have triangular faces.
2. 12
3. 25 x 250
4. 42
5. 283
6. unlikely
7. hexagonal pyramid
8. 8
9. Jack: | 40 bookmarks |

   Sue: | 28 bookmarks |

   Difference: | | 12 bookmarks

   Each shares: 12 ÷ 2 = 6
   So, Jack should give 6 bookmarks to Sue.
10. **1** David→A→D→E→Jill   4
    2 David→A→D→G→Jill   4
    3 David→A→B→E→Jill   4
    4 David→C→D→G→Jill   4
    5 David→C→F→G→Jill   4
    6 David→C→D→E→Jill   4
    All the routes have the same distance.

Practice 8

1.
2. three quarters of a litre
3. 6
4. 40 cm
5. 2 units left, 3 units up
6. 16
7. about 1 year
8. Pattern rule: + 4, – 1
   First pattern: 1, 5, 4, 8, 7
   (Suggested answer for second pattern)
   Second pattern: 10, 14, 13, 17
9.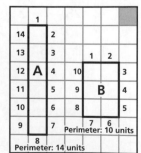

   The flower bed with a smaller perimeter needs less fencing. She should choose B, which has the dimensions of 2 units by 3 units.

Practice 9

1. rectangular pyramid
2. 2 in 6
3. three fourths
4. 13
5. 22
6. 40 minutes
7. millimetres
8. 12
9. about 1 month
10.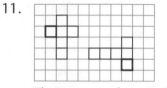

    one third broken
    one fourth for cookies
    eggs left

    Mrs. Green has 6 eggs left.

11.

    The nets can form cubes.

Practice 10

1. 2
2. 6
3. 6 km
4. She needs 5¢ more to get what she wants.
5. 24
6. 125
7. 13
8. C
9. Circle: 38 ; 47 ; 56 ; 65 ; 74 ; 83 ; 92
   The numbers go down to the left diagonally. The digits in the tens columns increase by 1 each time, and the digits in the ones columns decrease by 1 each time.
10.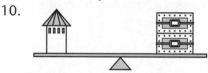

    Two chests weigh 2 kg.

    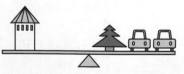

    One tree and two cars weigh 2 kg in total.

Practice 11

1. 24
2. They have exactly one pair of equal angles.
3. 5 m, 9 m
4. 4 + 4 = 8

ISBN: 978-1-897164-78-5

5. reflection   6. 1 L

7. July 6   8. 5

9.

Card Number	Tally
1	⫲⫲ II
2	⫲⫲ IIII
3	⫲⫲ ⫲⫲ IIII

It is most likely to draw a "3" card and least likely to draw a "1" card. So the set of cards should have the most "3" cards and the least "1" cards. Janet might have set A.

10.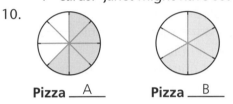

Pizza _A_   **Pizza** _B_

No, Uncle Sam is not correct, because four sixths is greater than five eighths as we can see in the diagrams.

Practice 12

1. 6 weeks   2. $42 \div 6 = 7$

3. $\dfrac{12}{20}$ 4. 8

5. $\dfrac{4}{8}$ 6. 2

7. likely   8. 10

9. Perimeter of the park: 500 (m)
Total distance travelled: 500 x 3 = 1500 (m)
So they will travel a total of 1500 m.

10.

Units	Triangles	Circles
1	2	3
2	4	6
3	6	9
4	8	12

Following the pattern, 6 units can be made with 12 triangles. Since there are 18 circles in 6 units, 18 circles are needed to go with 12 triangles.

Practice 13

1. It is equally likely to draw an odd number card or an even number card.

2. B, D, and E   3. 5 + 5 + 5

4. 114   5. add 3, subtract 1

6. 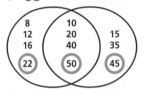   7. 20 cm

8. 30 ; 40 ; 20 ; 50

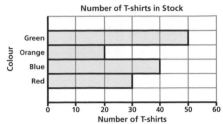

No, he should order orange T-shirts the most, because it has the highest sales figure.

9. (Suggested answers for examples)

The numbers in the overlapping part are divisible by 2 and 5.

Practice 14

1. 2, 5, 11, 23, 47

2. rectangular faces and pyramids

3. 14   4. 15

5. 12:20 p.m.

6. The arrow makes a $\dfrac{1}{4}$ counterclockwise turn each time.

7. 4   8. 5

9.

Sun	Mon	Tue	Wed	Thur	Fri	Sat
1	2	3	4	5	6	7
+1	+1	+1	+1	+1	+1	

She will buy 5 bags of chips on Thursday, 6 bags on Friday and 7 bags on Saturday.
Total: 1 + 2 + 3 + 4 + 5 + 6 + 7 = 28 (bags)
She will buy 28 bags of chips in a week.

10. We expect the pointer to land on "blue" half of 60 times, which is 30 times. The number of times the pointer landing on "red" or "green" should be the same. Therefore, Brian's prediction is the most reasonable.

Assessment

1. 438

2. between 400 and 500

3. 96   4. pentagonal prism

5. 17, 20, 19, 22, 21

6. 1 dime and 3 nickels

7. 2 out of 6   8. 12 cm

9. 4 units right, then 3 units down

10. 39 − 12 = 27

ISBN: 978-1-897164-78-5

11. 119
12. 10
13. –11°C
14. 4
15. It has 4 triangular faces.
16. 14
17. $\frac{3}{5}$
18. 6 + 6 + 6 + 6 + 6
19. B
20. 28
21. 6
22. 5
23. 4
24. 20
25. 6 kg
26. 7:57 p.m.
27. 10
28. 13
29. Pattern rule for perimeter:
Start at 4. Add 2 each time.
Pattern rule for number of pebbles:
Start at 5. Add 5 each time.
There are 25 pebbles in the frame that has 5 squares, and the perimeter of the frame is 12 units.

30.

Yes, it is possible. The figures are pentagonal pyramid and triangular prism. A pentagonal pyramid has 10 edges, 1 pentagon face, and 5 triangular faces. A triangular prism has 9 edges, 2 triangular faces, and 3 rectangular faces.

31.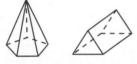

Number of Hours Spent Watching TV in a Week

No, Jill is wrong. Since the number of people surveyed is 22, we can use subtraction to find the missing data. The missing data is 5 people.

32. There are 2 balls with a "1", 3 balls with a "2", 2 balls with a "3", and 3 balls with a "4".

The probability of drawing a "1" is $\frac{2}{10}$, a "2" is $\frac{3}{10}$, a "3" is $\frac{2}{10}$, and a "4" is $\frac{3}{10}$.

So, the number on the ball might be 2 or 4.

33. Steven has: 4 dollars and 34 cents
Steven's sister has: 5 dollars and 30 cents
Total: 9 dollars and 64 cents
They are able to buy a storybook.

34. No, Jenny is wrong. The perimeter of figure A is 16 units, and the perimeter of figure B is 20 units.

35. There are 5 red beads and 4 blue beads in each necklace. 40 red beads are needed to make 8 necklaces.

36. (Suggested answer)
1st key: 4 units left and 1 unit down
2nd key: 4 units down
3rd key: 4 units left and 1 unit up
Chest: 3 units up

ISBN: 978-1-897164-78-5